Lil Legends

Number Tracing & Activity Book

Writing Practice for Kids

level 1

OSWAAL BOOKS®

LEARNING MADE SIMPLE

India's First Pre-Writing Program

Lil Legends

An imprint of Oswaal Books Learning Pvt. Ltd.

PUBLISHED BY

OSWAAL BOOKS & LEARNING PVT. LTD.

INDIA OFFICE
1/11, Sahitya Kunj, M.G. Road,
Agra - 282002, (UP) India

UK OFFICE
1010, Cambourne
Cambridge, Cambridgeshire
CB 23#6DP, United Kingdom

Phone: 0562-2857671
E-mail: contact@oswaalbooks.com
Website: www.Oswaalbooks.com
ISBN: **9789357287050**
Printed at: **Paras Offset Pvt. Ltd., Kundli-131028**

Number Tracing
& Activity Book

Writing Practice for Kids

This Book Belongs to

....

Attention Parents...

Introducing India's first Pre-writing Program

Our proprietary writing program, is designed to help toddlers master their pre-writing skills. The program is based on five S-philosophies:

1. Skill Escalation:

All tracing and numeracy activities advance in skill gradually, requiring one to follow the guide in its natural sequence.

2. Strategic Sequence:

The program follows the natural flow of numbers, allowing children to understand the concept of numbers. After exploring numbers, the child progress to explore 2D shapes in varied sizes.

3. Smart Dot Guidance:

All patterns have smart guiding dots that are indicators on where to start, where to trace to and when one must lift off their writing instrument. All smart dots are numbered and coloured.

Starting Point: • (Green Dot)

End Point: • (Red Dot)

4. Stimulation based Practice:

The guide will not just help the child master number tracing but learn the basic concepts of numbers such as number recognition, object counting, dot counting and finger counting. The guide also allows children to explore shapes and associated objects with it. It also includes over 15 logic and math activities to further their learning.

5. Self- Appreciation:

The guide awards children with a certification to celebrate their learning and their enhanced writing skills.

Writing is an important tool, that must be introduced with great care and responsibility.

This guided pre-writing series is India's first pre-writing program that will allow parents and schools to simplify writing for their children and making pre-writing more structured, effective and fun. The program is aimed to help millions of toddlers to successfully yet responsibly embark on their writing journey.

Our goal in this series is to help parents:

- Learn about the age-appropriate grip goals for children
- Identify grip-appropriate writing instruments for children
- Embark on your child's writing journey in a structured and guided manner
- Simplify learning

Before we start on our child's writing journey, it is important that as parents and educators we are informed about some key developmental milestones.

What is a Pincer Grip? Why Do I need to know about it?

Pincer Grip is a grip between the index finger or middle finger and the thumb to grasp an object. Children are not born with this grip developed and first signs of development start around 9-10 months and this grip is fully developed around the age of 5-6 years.

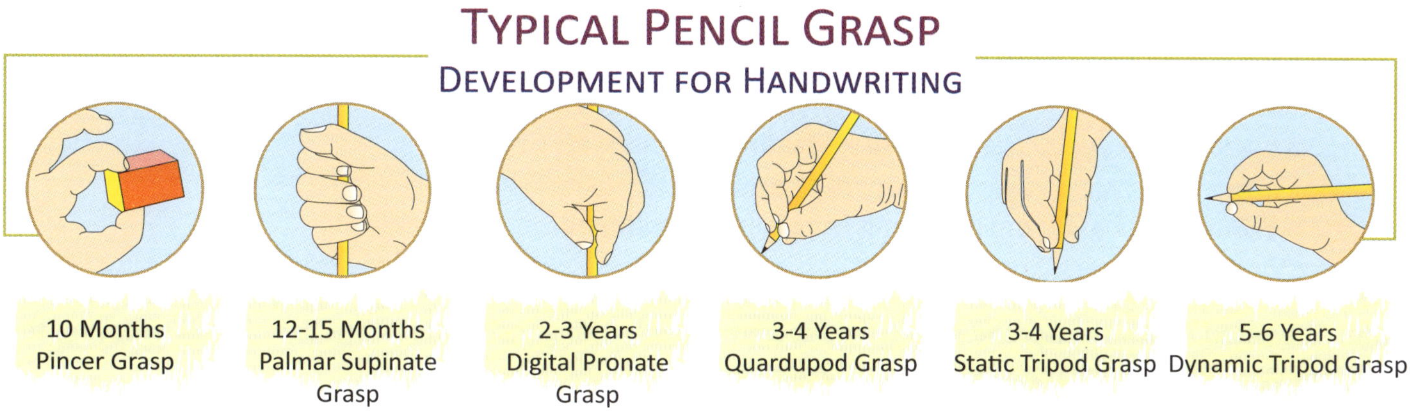

What happens if a child is made to write before the grip is fully developed?

- Child may develops low self esteem and confidence incase unable to cope with writing.
- Child may becomes reluctant and unmotivated towards their learning.
- Child may adopts a poor handwriting.
- Child is often misdiagnosed with learning disorders, such as dysgraphia, dyslexia, due to their inability to cope with the existing writing programs, underdeveloped visual-motor skills.
- Causes muscle strain and potential loss of muscle dexterity.

Suggested activities to improve pincer grip development

- Pick and sort objects
- Tearing waste paper
- Pinching bubble wrap, clay, edible dough
- Lacing activities
- Squishing pomegranate, grapes and similar food items
- Open scribbling & mark making
- Colouring on vertical panel

"Before we ever put a pencil in a child's hands, those hands should dig, climb, press, push, squish, twist, and pinch in a wide array of environments and with a variety of materials."

Dr. Amanda Morgan, a world renowned early child expert.

Writing Instrument Guidelines

While their grips are still under development, children can participate in early writing by choosing the correct writing instruments:

- 10 months - 14 months: Ball Crayons (110 mm) & Jumbo Egg Chalk
- 15 months - 20 months: Grasp Crayons (33 mm), Fat Chalk, Dot Markers
- 21 months - 30 months: Grip Crayons (21 mm), Dot Markers, Golf Pencils With Triangular Grips
- 2.5 years - 3.5 years: Thick Crayons (11 mm), Golf Pencils With Grips
- 3.5 years - 4.5 years: Triangular or Hexagonal Pencils with Grip
- 4.5 years: Triangular or Hexagonal Pencils (Grip Optional)

Note: The listed width measurements of the recommended writing instruments are based after studying the effectiveness of the writing tools available for children.

You have picked Level 1: Number Tracing & Activity Book

This guide is focused on helping children get introduced to basic concepts of early mathematics and help children learn to trace numbers and shapes.

(1) Numbers 0-10 will be introduced with finger counting, dot counting and object counting.

(2) All numbers and shapes will be traced to the appropriate size and with smart dots.

(3) Children will learn to relate daily objects with respective shapes.

(4) Engage in 15+ logic and counting activities that will help re-enforce concepts of early mathematics.

Zen Number Zero

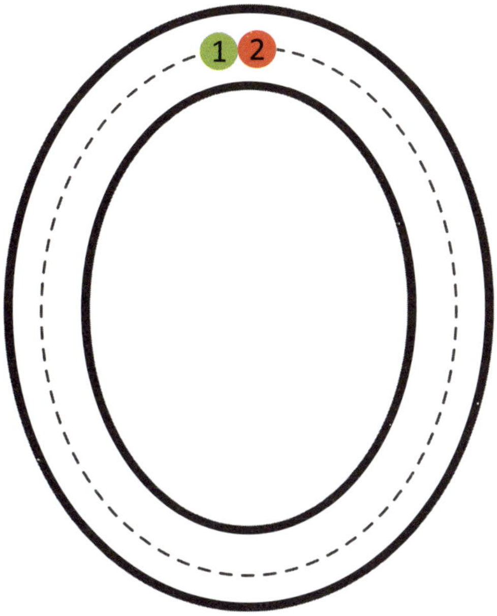

0

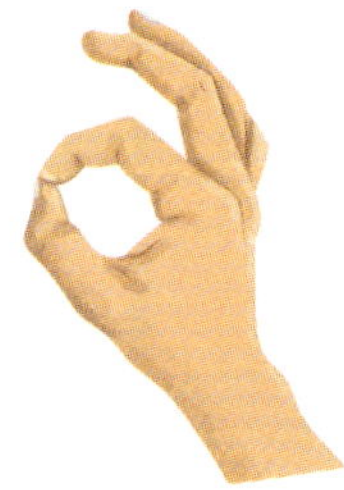

Trace over the smart dots and learn to recognise and count.

Inspiring Number One

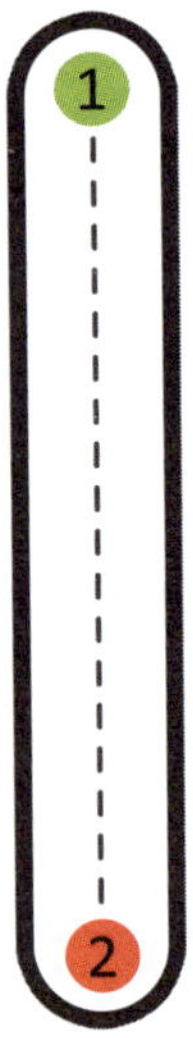

Trace over the smart dots and learn to recognise and count.

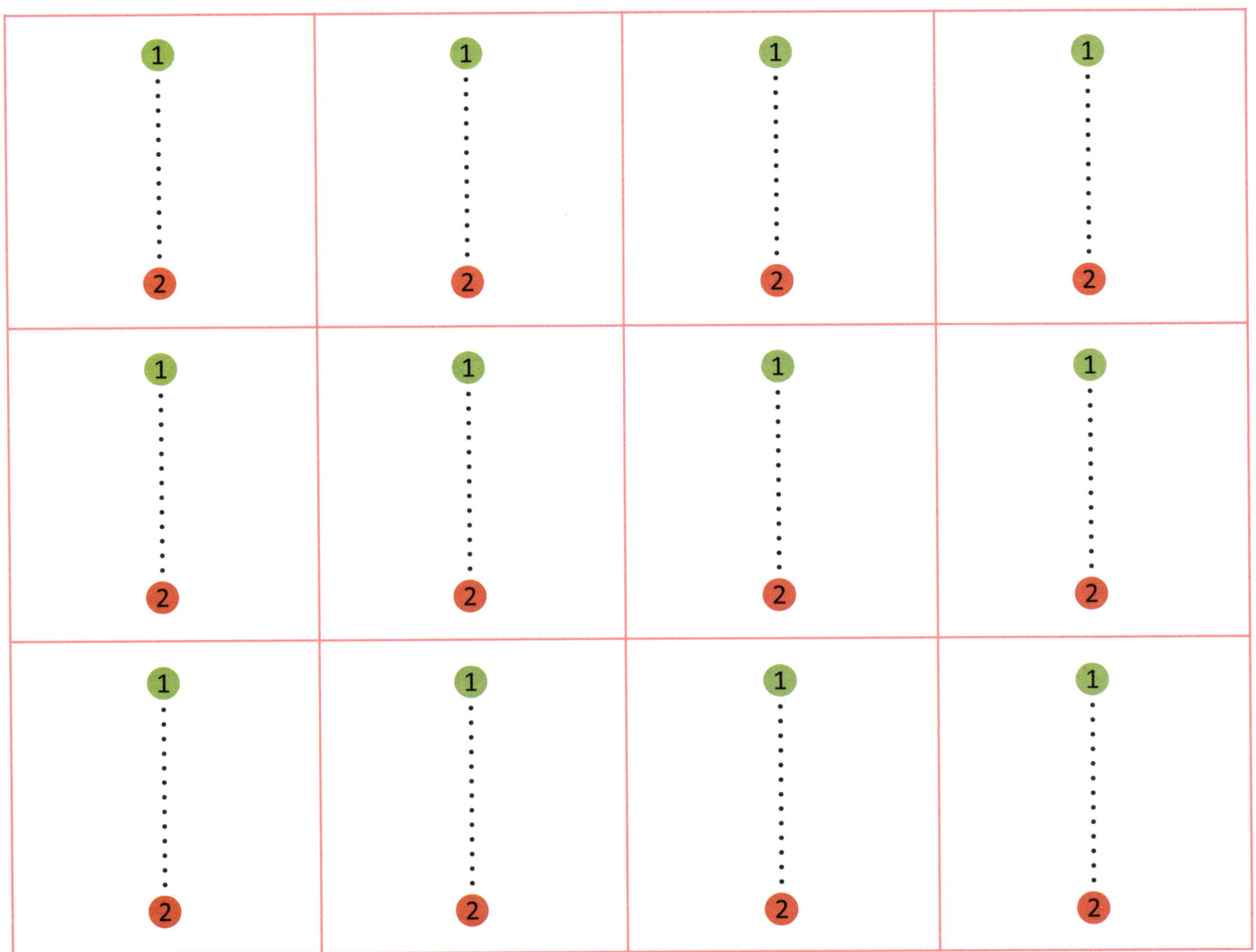

Talented Number Two

Trace over the smart dots and learn to recognise and count.

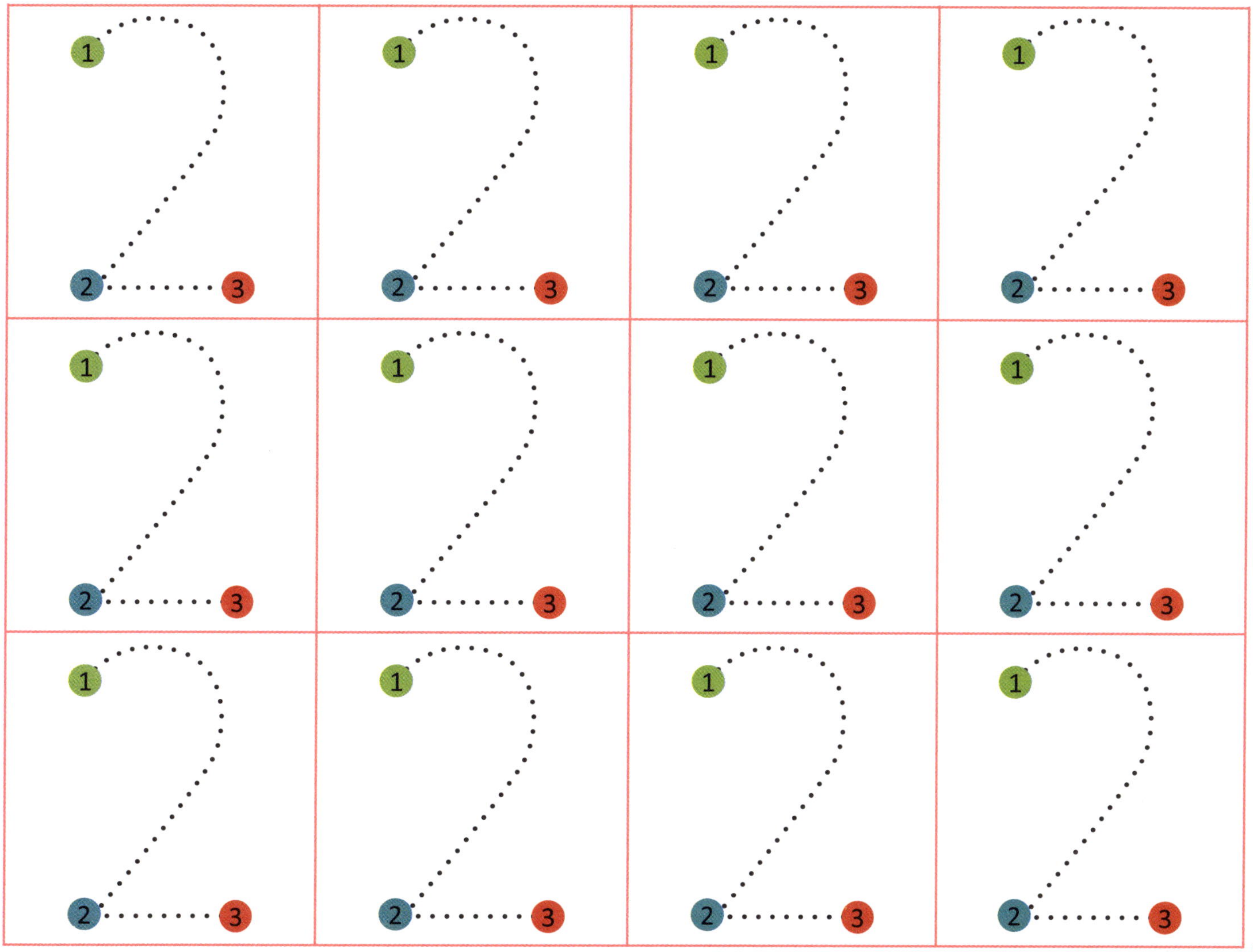

Terrific Number Three

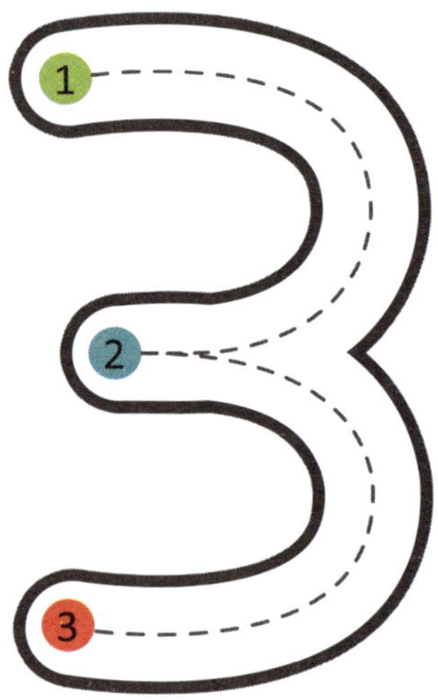

Trace over the smart dots and learn to recognise and count.

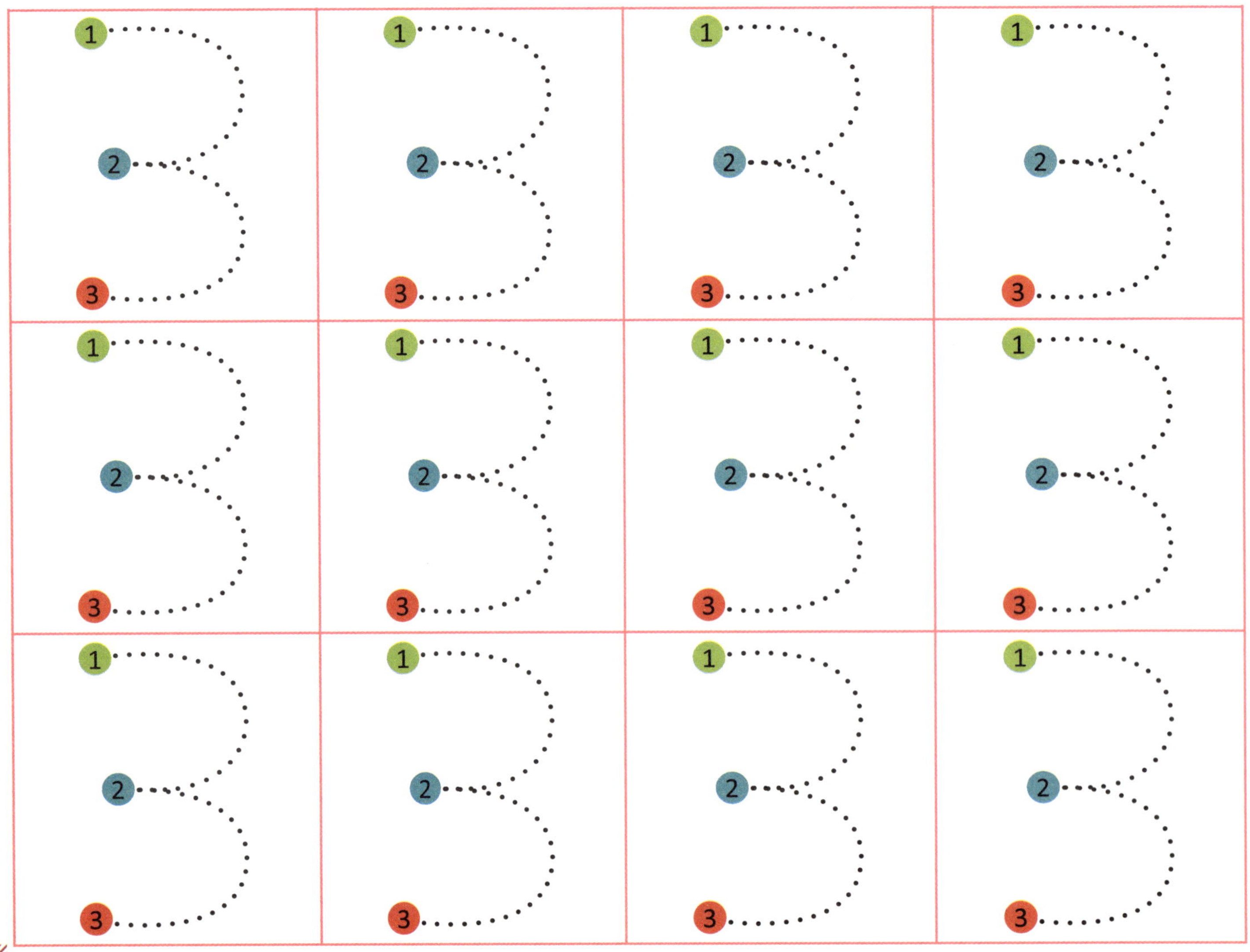

Fearless Number Four

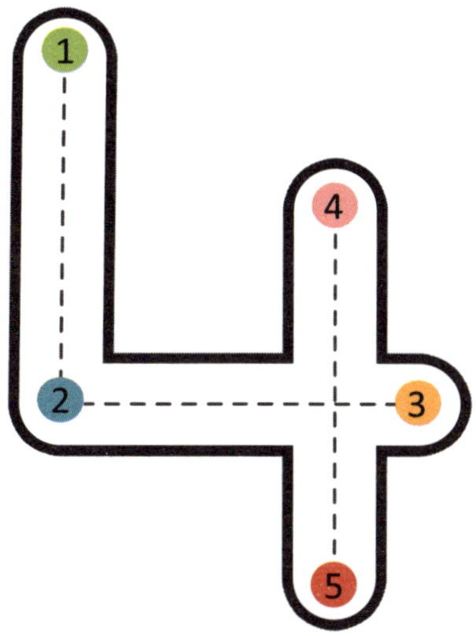

Trace over the smart dots and learn to recognise and count.

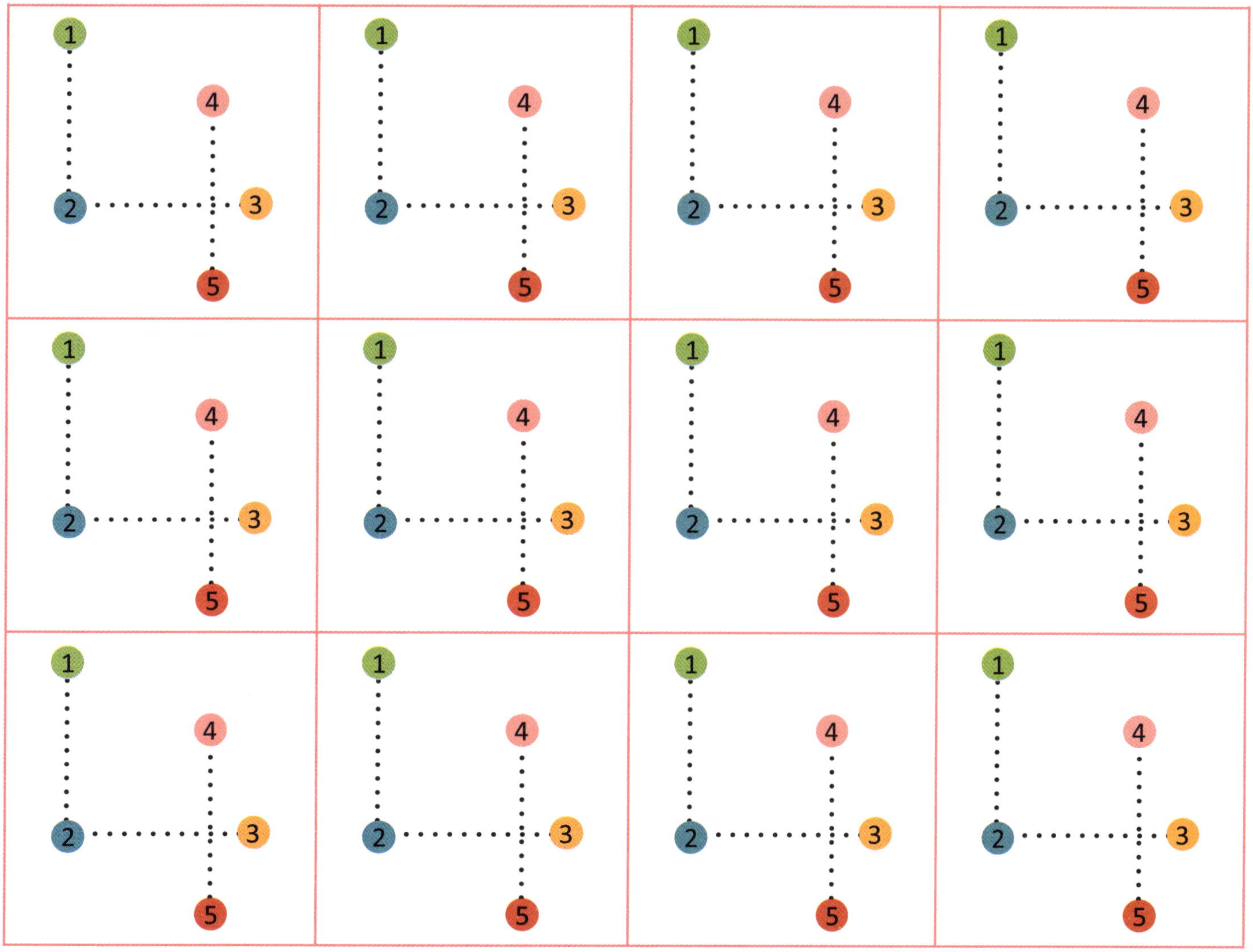

Fantastic Number Five

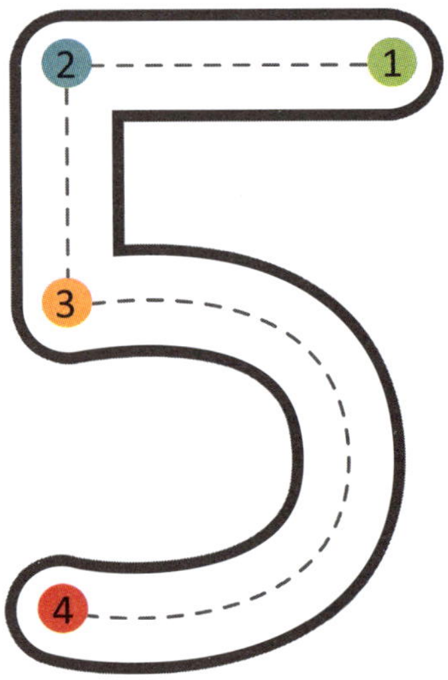

Trace over the smart dots and learn to recognise and count.

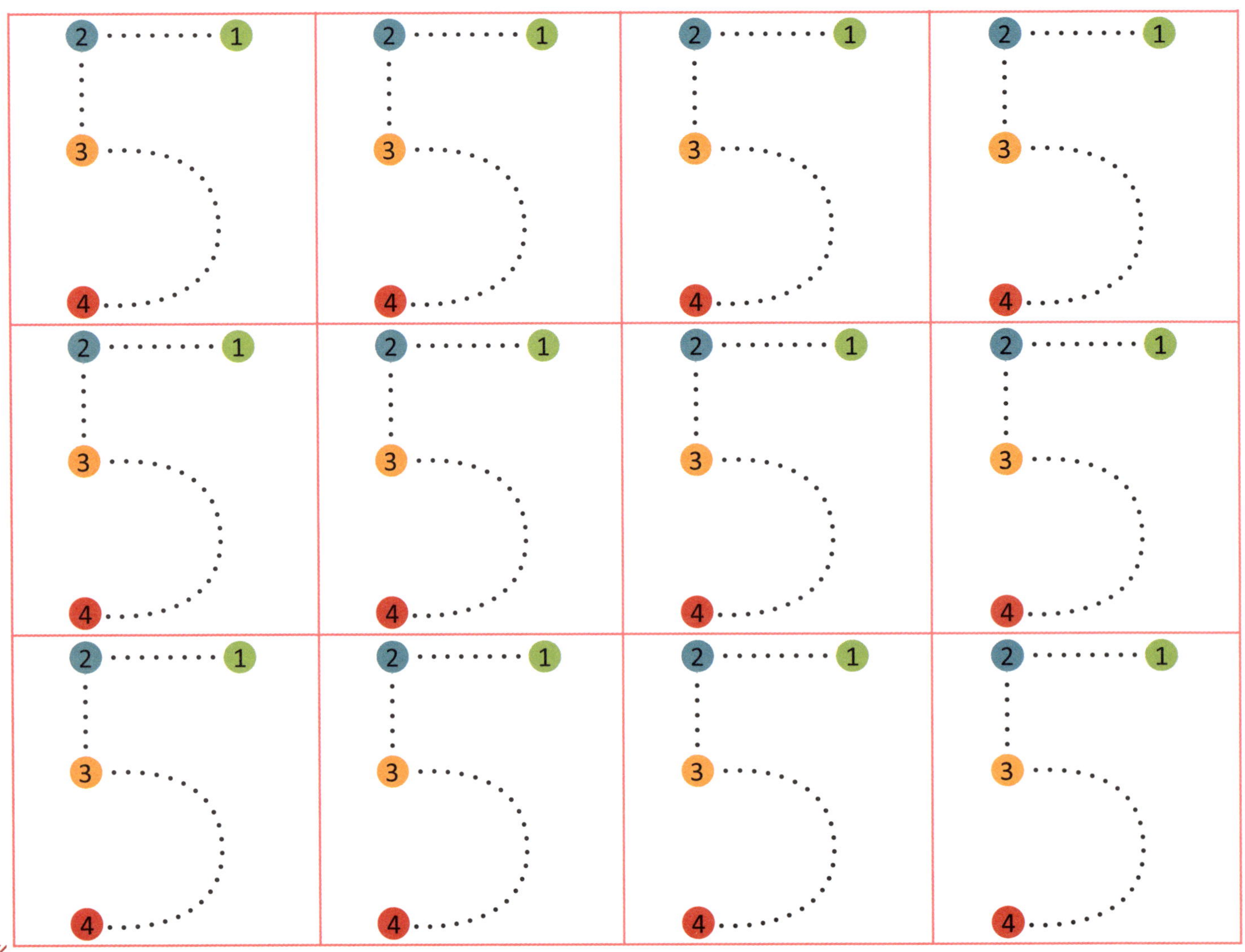

Steady Number Six

Trace over the smart dots and learn to recognise and count.

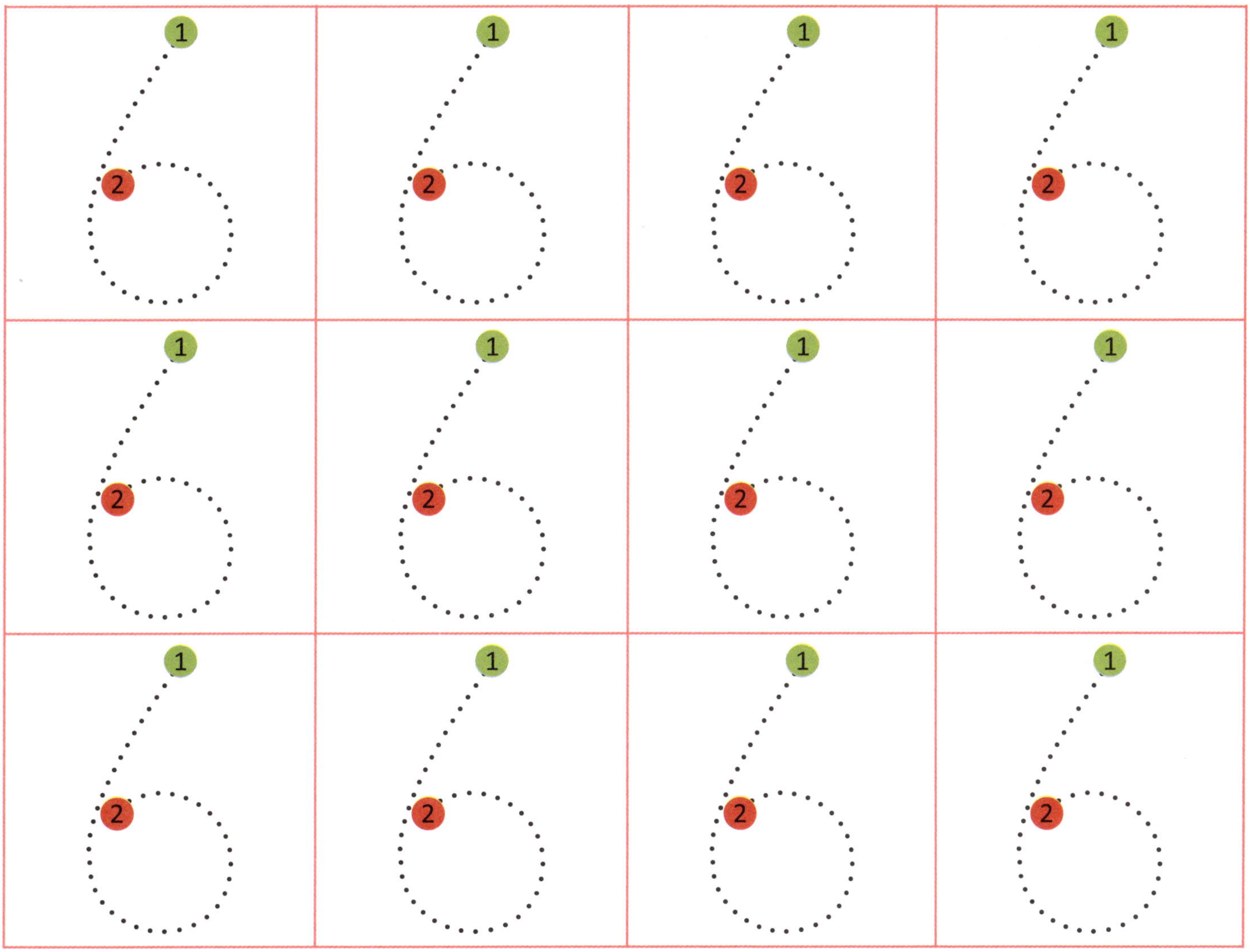

Super Number Seven

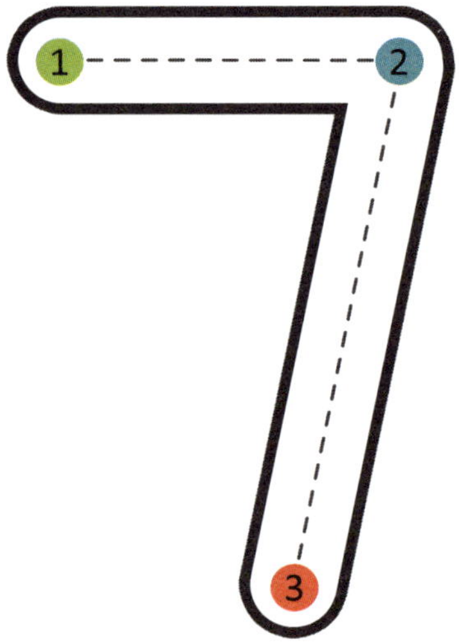

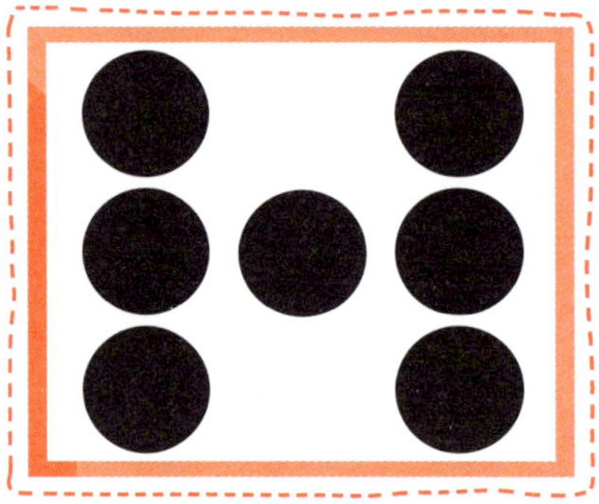

Trace over the smart dots and learn to recognise and count.

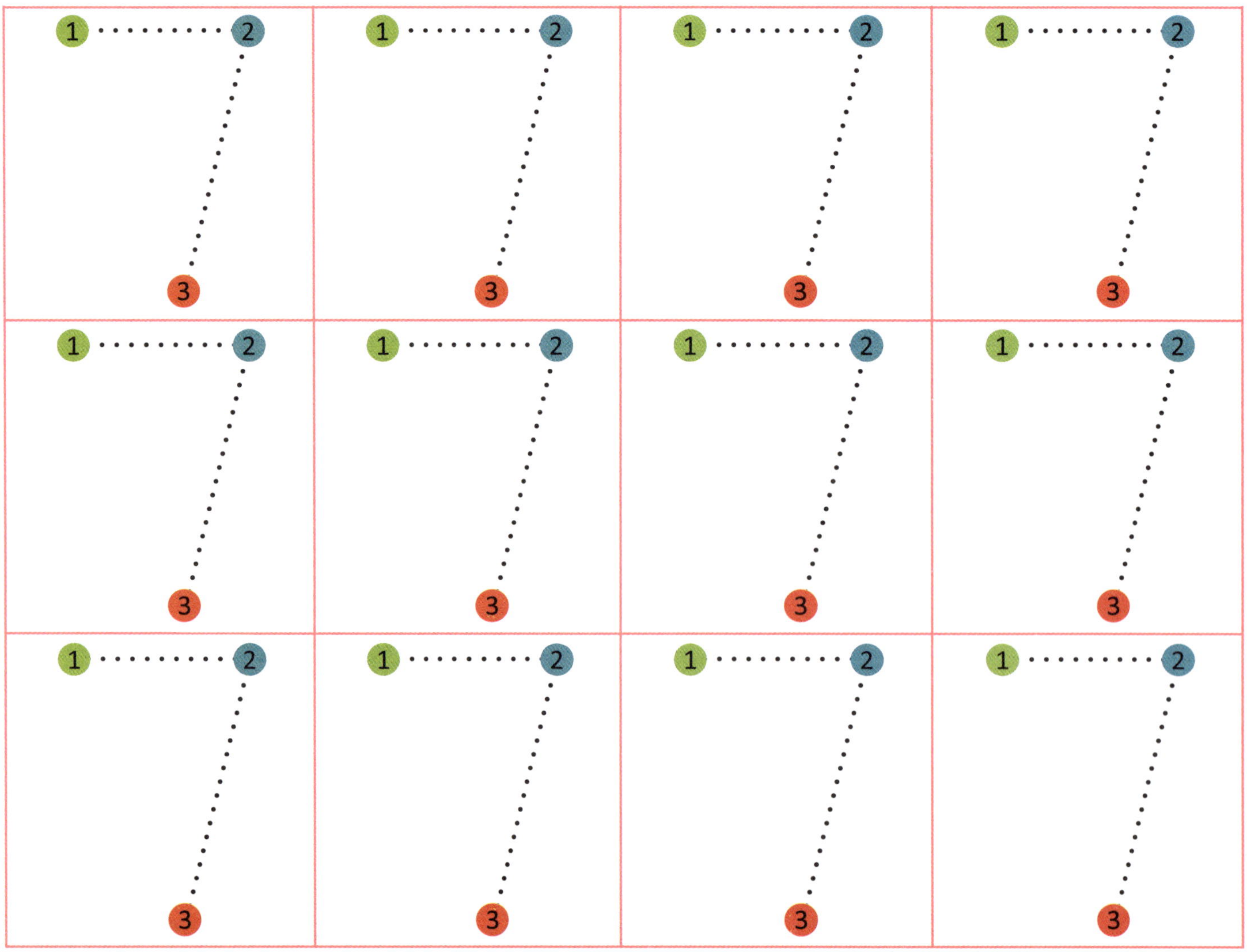

Enthusiastic Number Eight

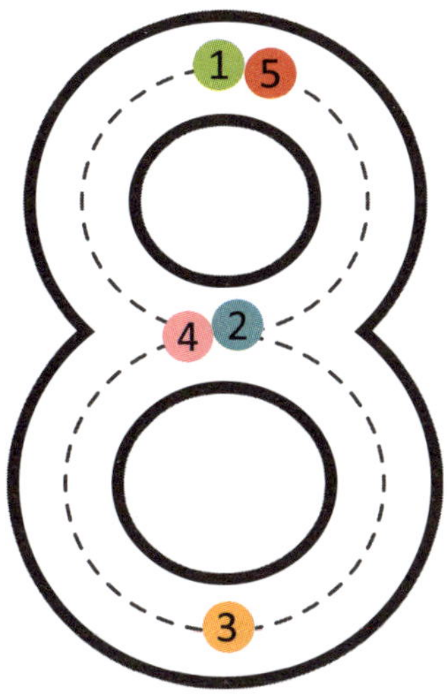

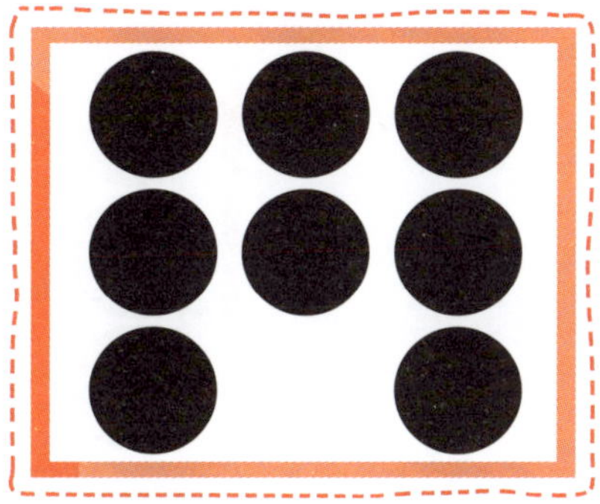

Trace over the smart dots and learn to recognise and count.

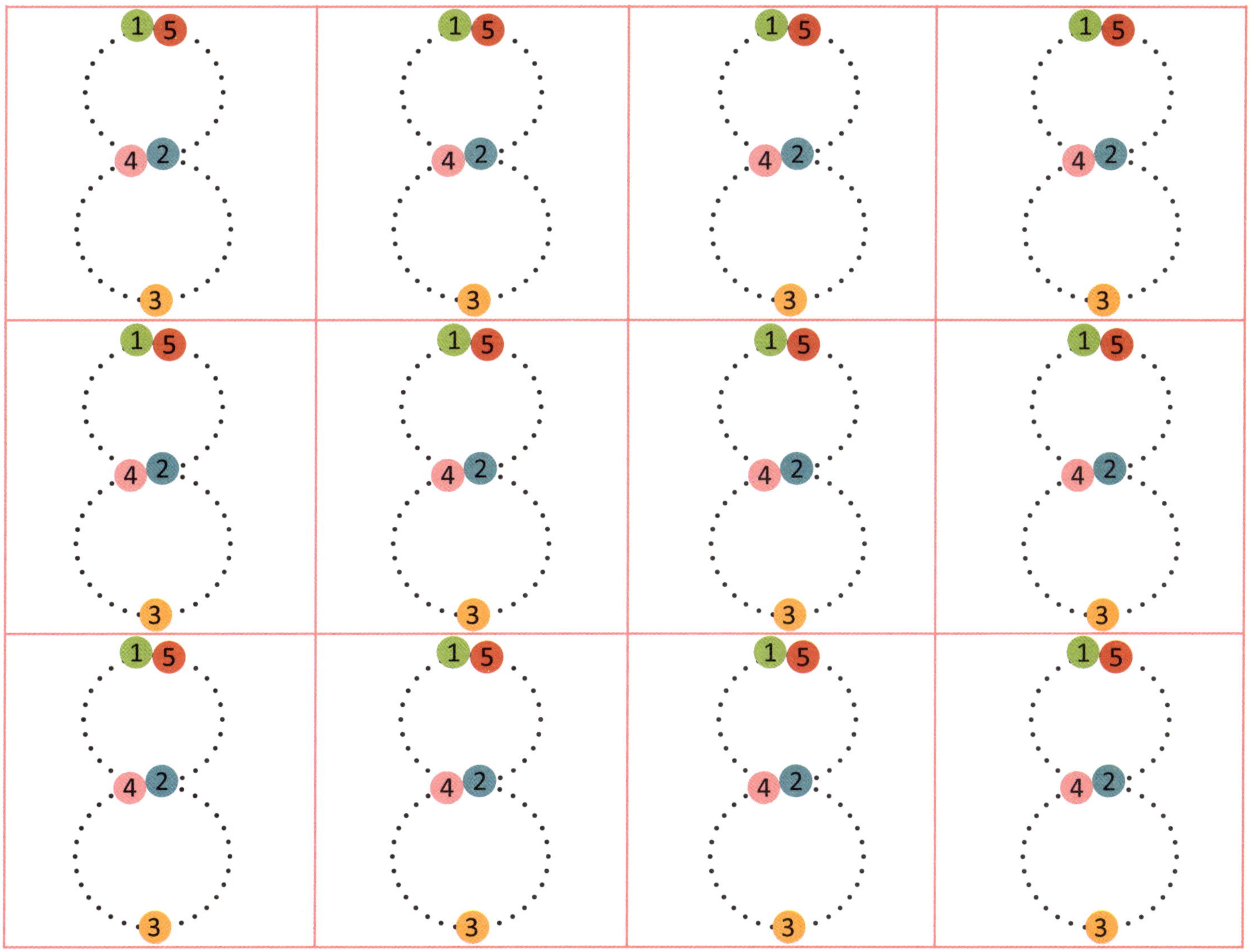

Novel Number Nine

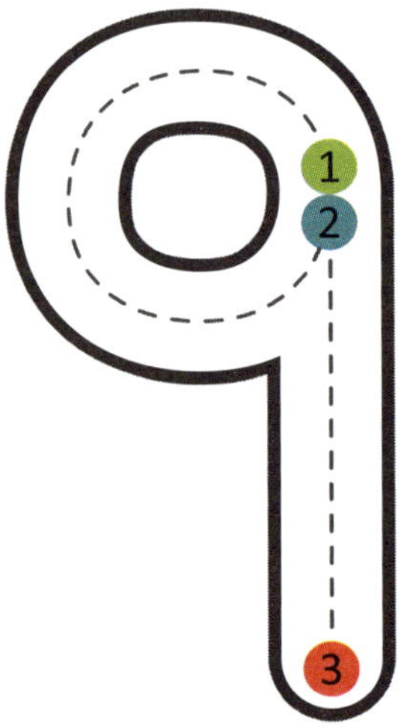

Trace over the smart dots and learn to recognise and count.

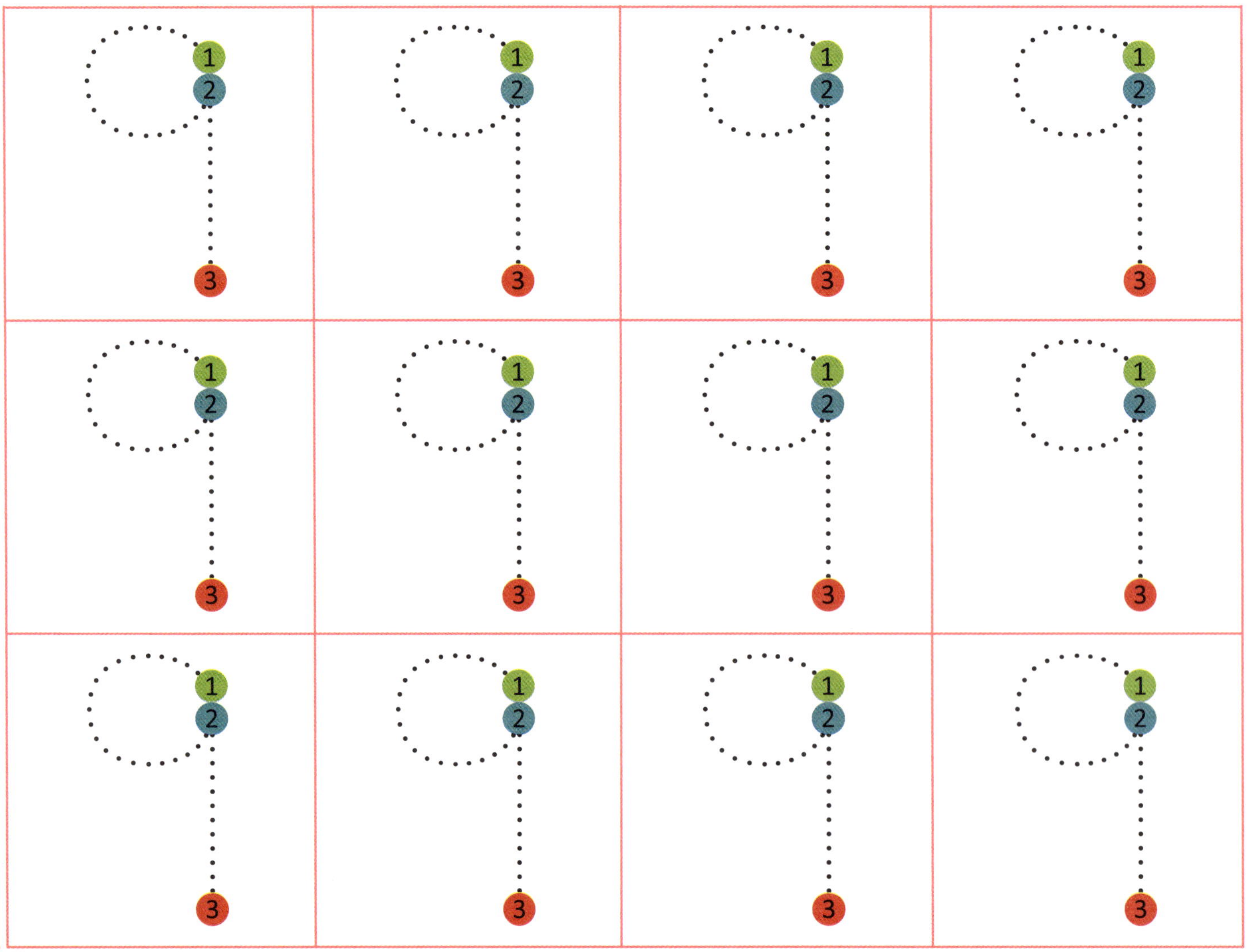

Thriving Number Ten

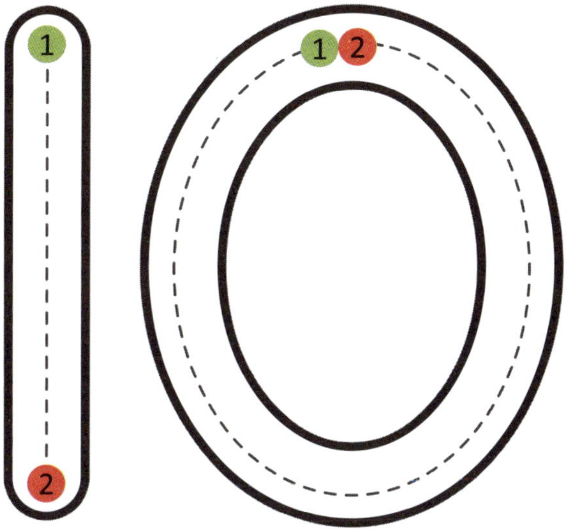

Trace over the smart dots and learn to recognise and count.

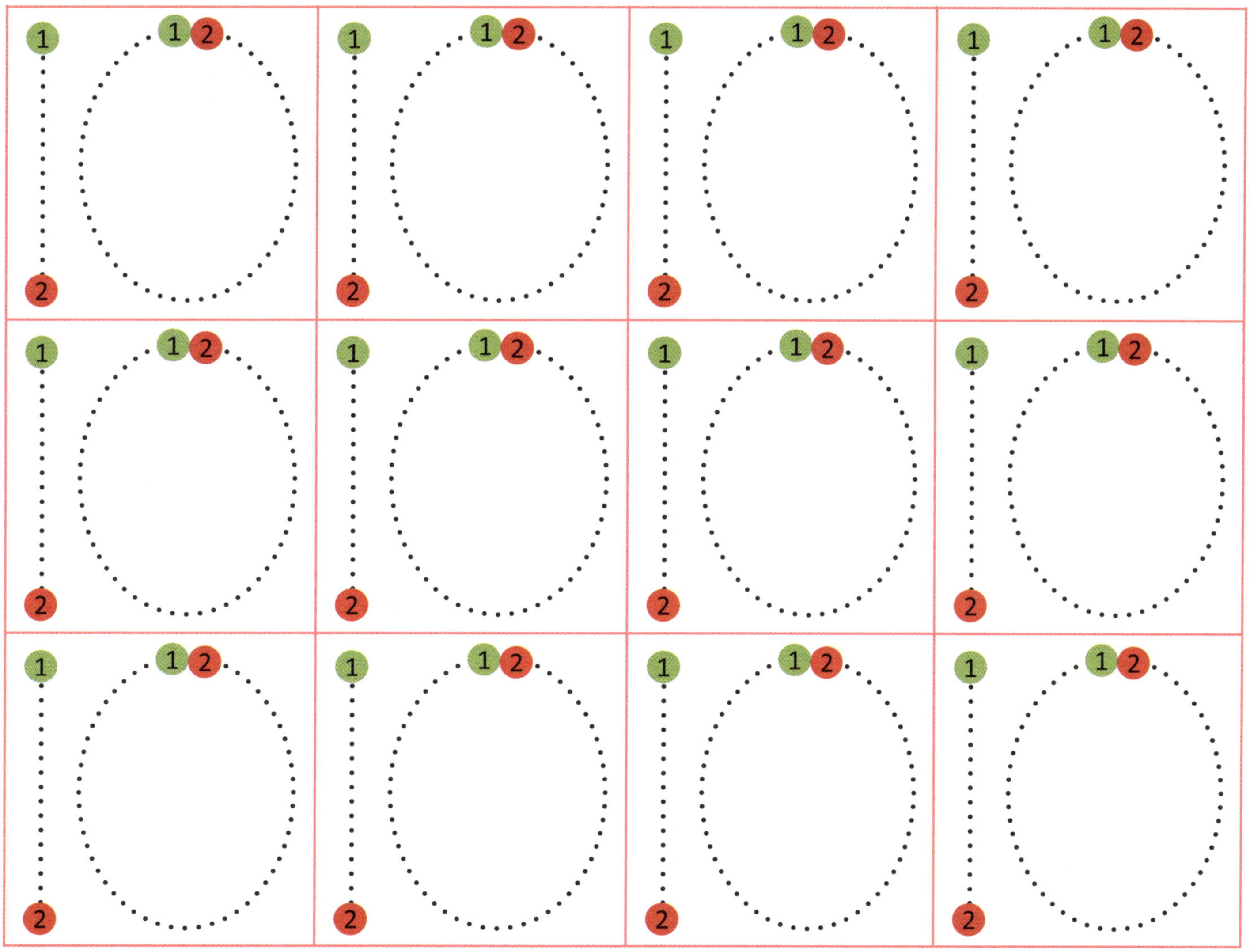

CIRCLE

TYRE

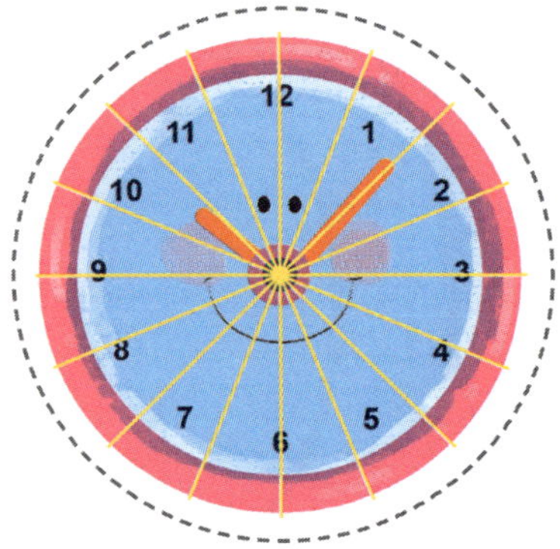

CLOCK

HEART

GIFT BOX

LEAF

STAR

STARFISH

FLOWER

PIZZA

COOKIE

COIN

STRAWBERRY

BISCUIT

CANDY

WAND

STAR

BADGE

SQUARE

WINDOW

CARROM BOARD

TRIANGLE

MOUNTAIN

CHRISTMAS TREE

RECTANGLE

DOOR

PAINTING

PICTURE

TOAST

DICE

TRAFFIC CONE

RECYCLE SIGN

WATERMELON

CHOCOLATE

ENVELOPE

STAMP

PENTAGON

KENNEL

BIRD HOUSE

HEXAGON

DUSTBIN

BADGE

DIAMOND

KITE

SAFETY SIGN

DIAMOND

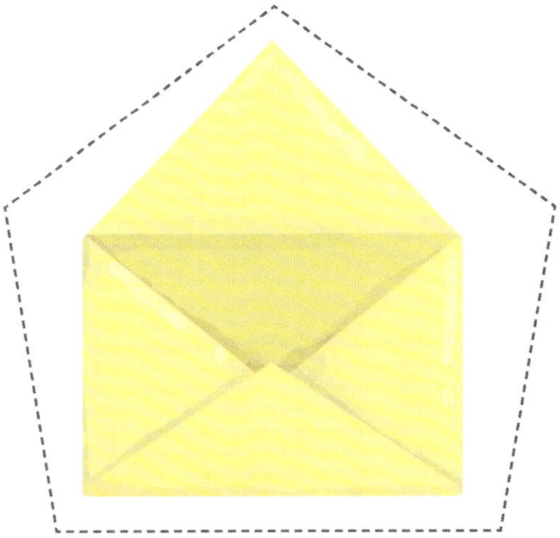

OPEN ENVELOPE

CUP CAKE

GEMSTONE

SNOWFLAKE

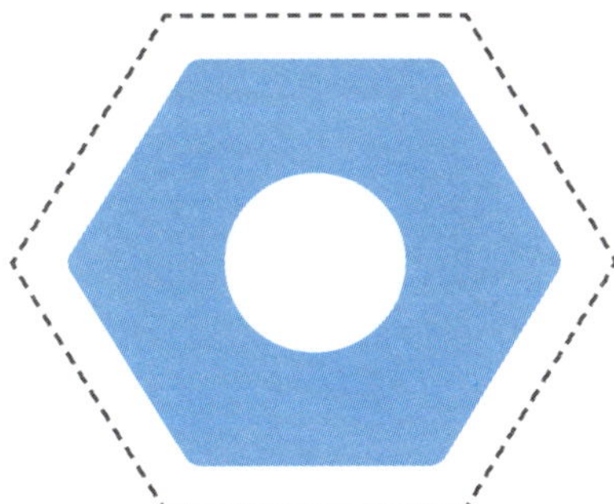

BOLT

WASP

CRESCENT

MOON

BANANA

CROISSANT

You are doing amazing! Now, let's try and trace all numbers from 0 to 10 once together.

0	1	2	3
4	5	6	7
8	9	10	

YOU
DID
IT!

Colour the Number

Find the number two and colour them in your favourite colour.

Count & Colour

Count the balloons in the photo and colour the right number of balloons for every colour.

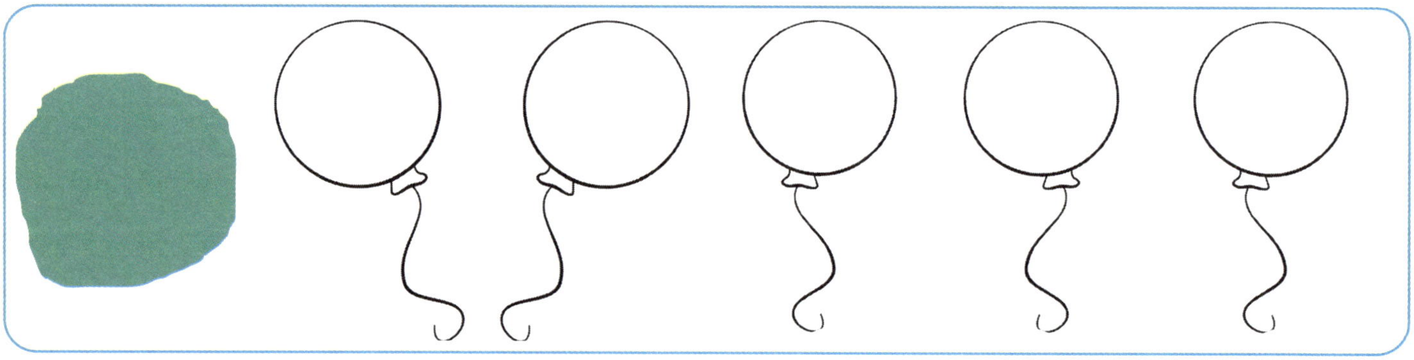

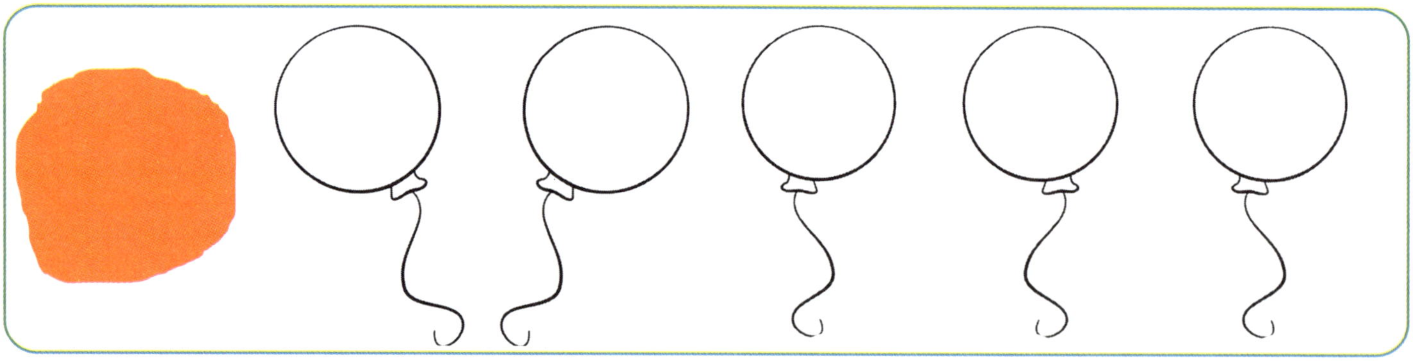

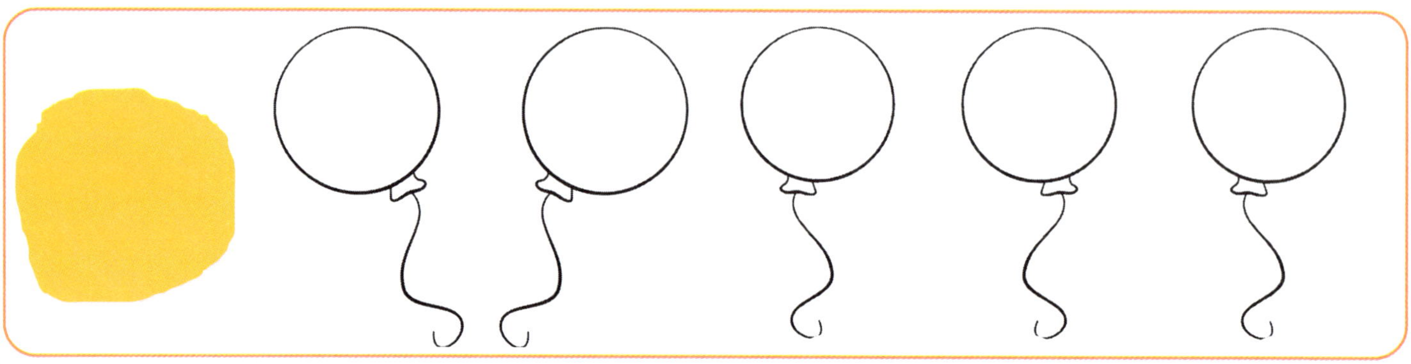

Count & Match!

Match each group of elements to the right number.

1 2 3 4

Count & Mark

Mark the box with the right number of sea animals!

3 6 1

6 5 4

4 3 5

6 3 2

Recognise & Colour

Colour the specified number of boxes under each object.

5

4

2

3

Shapes & Patterns

Colour the specified number of shapes in each column.

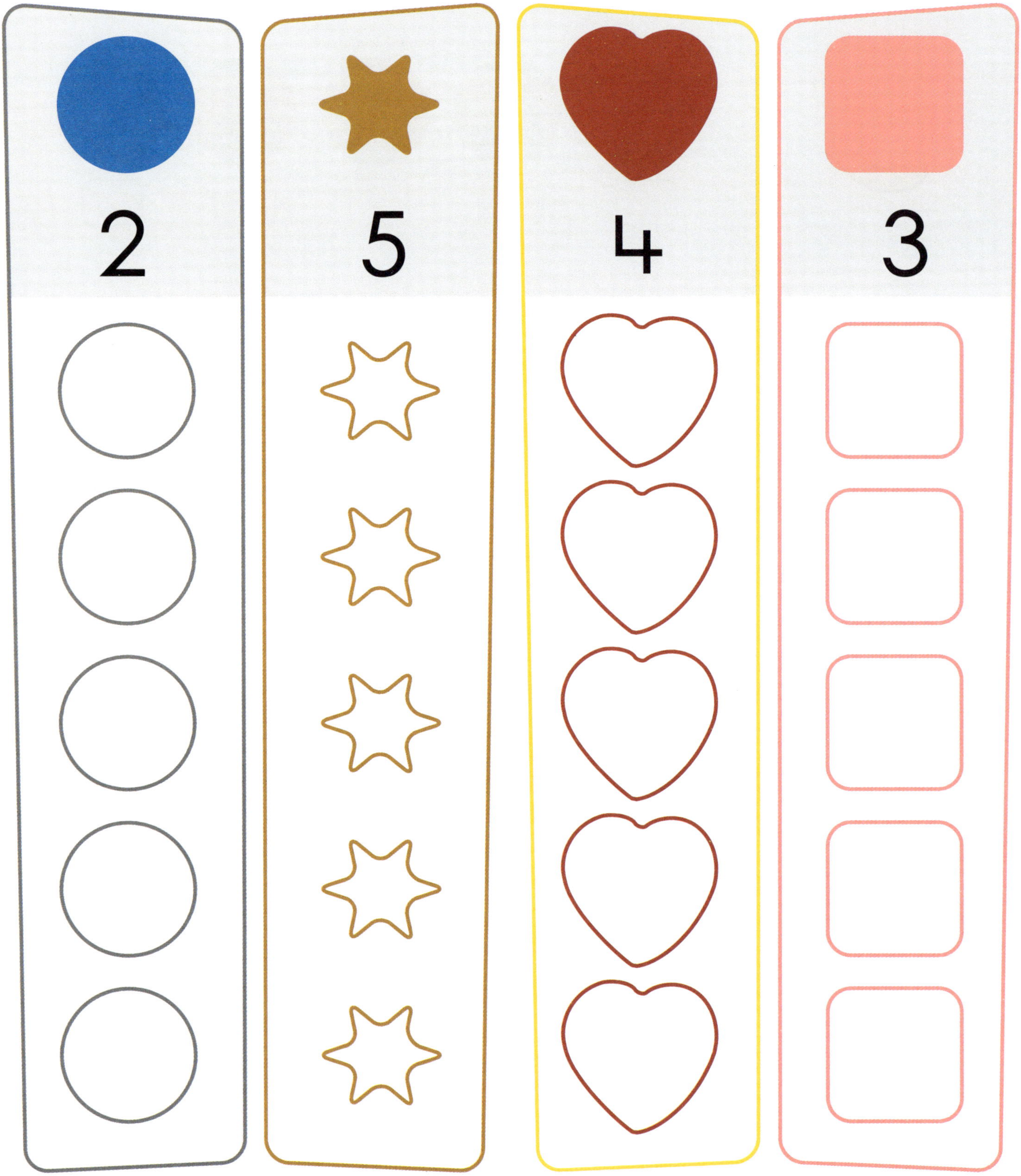

Cookie Monster

Treat yourself with a cookie after counting and tracing the right number of cookies in each jar.

4 5 6

6 7 8

8 9 10

10 11 12

4 5 6

6 7 8

Vegetable Farming

Help the farmer count the number of vegetables growing in his farm!

5 6 4

6 8 9

1 3 5

8 7 5

Everyday Shapes

Identify the shapes and match to the corresponding daily object.

Shapes & Shadows

Identify the shapes and match to their secret shadows!

Lil Legends

Certificate of

Achievement

This is to certify that .... has successfully completed the **Number Tracing & Activity Book.** He/She has also completed Level-1 of our Pre-writing Program.

OSWAAL BOOKS®
LEARNING MADE SIMPLE

Author Profile

Sonia Agarwal Bajaj

Sonia Agarwal Bajaj is a visionary new age edupreneur, who is making a profound impact in the field of education and skilling.

Sonia's passion to shape young hearts led her to start, Little Chipper International, an experiential learning based preschool in Agra. In a short span of time, this preschool has won many accolades and has been recognized amongst the top 5 Future Ready Preschools in India.

Committed to raising awareness about the importance of early education and helping parents embrace new learning and parenting techniques, Sonia hosts a spectrum of workshops across India. Her newest initiative includes conceptualising and authoring India's first structured pre-writing program for young children.

In addition to her contributions to the space in Early Education, she is the co-founder of Whiz league, an online skilling platform that offers celebrity led masterclasses at affordable prices. With over 1.2 million learning sessions, the platform grew to create its own learning management system that potentially helped hospitality and retail organizations train over 1 Lac staff members on a pan India basis. Sonia led the curriculum design and production for each of the 20 programs listed on the platform.

A Dhirubhai Ambani International School and Babson College alumnae, she has previously held a foray of responsibilities in the space of Ed-tech and fashion retail. Sonia has always been an advocate for the environment and she was a globally recognized founder of Whitenife, a platform that was dedicated to raising awareness on sustainable and ethical fashion.

With deep insight into the process and psychology of learning, Sonia is committed to further transform the education industry in times to come.